STEVE ROGERS
CAPTAIN AMERICA

collection editor: **JENNIFER GRÜNWALD**
assistant editor: **CAITLIN O'CONNELL**
associate managing editor: **KATERI WOODY**
editor, special projects: **MARK D. BEAZLEY**
vp production & special projects: **JEFF YOUNGQUIST**
svp print, sales & marketing: **DAVID GABRIEL**
book designer: **ADAM DEL RE**

editor in chief: **AXEL ALONSO**
chief creative officer: **JOE QUESADA**
president: **DAN BUCKLEY**
executive producer: **ALAN FINE**

Captain America created by
JOE SIMON & JACK KIRBY

Steve ★ Rogers
CAPTAIN AMERICA
EMPIRE BUILDING

★ WRITER ★

NICK SPENCER

—— CIVIL WAR II: THE OATH ——

★ ARTISTS ★

ROD REIS WITH

PHIL NOTO, RAFFAELE IENCO, SZYMON KUDRANSKI & DONO SÁNCHEZ-ALMARA

★ LETTERER ★
VC's CHRIS ELIOPOULOS

★ COVER ART ★
JEFF DEKAL

—— CAPTAIN AMERICA: STEVE ROGERS #12-16 ——

★ ARTISTS ★

JAVIER PINA AND ANDRES GUINALDO & SCOTT HANNA [#12];
RO STEIN & TED BRANDT [#13]; JESÚS SAIZ [#14];
JAVIER PINA AND ANDRES GUINALDO [#15]; AND
KEVIN LIBRANDA, YILDIRAY CINAR AND JON MALIN [#16]

★ COLOR ARTIST ★
RACHELLE ROSENBERG

★ LETTERER ★
VC's CHRIS ELIOPOULOS

★ COVER ART ★

SIMONE BIANCHI [#12], ARTHUR ADAMS & JASON KEITH [#13],
ELIZABETH TORQUE [#14], GABRIELE DELL'OTTO [#15] AND DANIEL ACUÑA [#16]

★ ASSISTANT EDITOR ★
ALANNA SMITH

★ EDITOR ★
TOM BREVOORT

CIVIL WAR II: THE OATH

EAGLE ONE APPROACHING--

WE HAVE CLEARANCE TO LAND-- LOOK ALIVE!

S.H.I.E.L.D. HELICARRIER ILIAD.

ALL AGENTS, ALL SPECIALISTS-- HIDE YOUR BEERS AND CLOSE OUT THOSE FACEBOOK ACCOUNTS--

--CAPTAIN AMERICA IS ON DECK.

SIR!

AT EASE, SOLDIER.

GOOD EVENING, SIR--IT'S--IT'S ALL READY FOR YOU, JUST LIKE YOU ASKED.

THANK YOU.

IT'S AN HONOR, SIR--AND--IF I MAY SPEAK FREELY?

GO RIGHT AHEAD.

WE ALL WATCHED YOU THIS AFTERNOON, DOWN IN THE REC, SIR AND--IT'S JUST--

--IT'S GOOD TO BE INSPIRED AGAIN, YOU KNOW? BEEN, UM...A LOT OF TURNOVER THESE LAST FEW YEARS, IF YOU KNOW WHAT I MEAN--

I DO. AND THAT'S ABOUT TO END--

--I CAN PROMISE YOU THAT MUCH.

YES, SIR--WELL, YOUR GUEST--OR WHATEVER--IS RIGHT IN THERE. THE ROOM IS TOTALLY QUIET, SWEPT IT MYSELF. JUST LIKE YOU ASKED.

I GOT THAT PART.

YES, SIR. AND IF YOU NEED ANYTHING--WATER, JUICE, COFFEE--I GOTTA IMAGINE YOU'RE PRETTY BEAT AT THIS POINT--

YOU HAVE NO IDEA.

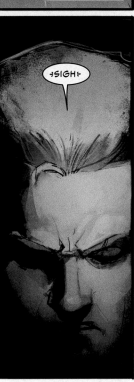

≠SIGH≠

CIVIL WAR

I

THE OATH

A NEW INHUMAN NAMED ULYSSES, WHO CLAIMED TO BE ABLE
TO SEE THE FUTURE, SPARKED A CIVIL WAR IN THE SUPER
HERO COMMUNITY. CAPTAIN MARVEL BELIEVED THAT IF SHE
HAD A CHANCE TO AVERT CATASTROPHE AND SAVE LIVES,
SHE HAD NO CHOICE BUT TO ACT. BUT IRON MAN BELIEVED
THAT ULYSSES' OWN BIASES AND EXPERIENCES INFLUENCED
HIS VISIONS, AND CLAIMED THAT ACTING ON THEM WAS NO
DIFFERENT THAN PROFILING.

A PREDICTION THAT THE YOUNGER SPIDER-MAN WOULD KILL
STEVE ROGERS LURED CAPTAIN MARVEL AND IRON MAN INTO
A VIOLENT FINAL CLASH OVER THE CAPITOL BUILDING--
A CLASH THAT LEFT TONY STARK CRITICALLY INJURED. IN
THE AFTERMATH OF THE BATTLE, ULYSSES EVOLVED BEYOND
HUMAN PERCEPTION AND VANISHED, ENDING THE WAR.

BUT CAPTAIN AMERICA WAS RECENTLY TURNED INTO AN
UNDERCOVER HYDRA AGENT BY A COSMIC CUBE, AND THERE
MAY BE EVEN DARKER THINGS ON THE HORIZON...

BELIEVE IT OR NOT, I *HAD* BEEN LOOKING FORWARD TO THIS, TONY-- I WAS JUST WAITING FOR THIS WAR TO END FOR MY CHANCE.

I WANTED US TO TALK. *ARGUE,* EVEN-- LIKE WE ALWAYS DID.

BUT I GUESS YOU'RE IN NO SHAPE TO DO THAT NOW.

I'M SO SORRY THAT THIS HAD TO HAPPEN TO YOU. ESPECIALLY LIKE THIS.

AND I KNOW YOU'RE GOING TO COME BACK FROM IT, SOMEDAY. YOU'RE GOING TO FIX YOURSELF--BECAUSE THAT'S THE KIND OF THING YOU *DO.* YOU REINVENT THE RULES. YOU CHANGE THE PARADIGMS. ANSWER TO NO ONE, NOT EVEN *DEATH.*

I'M JEALOUS OF THAT SOMETIMES, YOU KNOW. WHEN YOU PLEDGE YOUR LIFE AND LOYALTY TO AN INSTITUTION, THE WAY I'VE ALWAYS DONE, YOU LEARN TO...EXIST WITHIN ITS LIMITATIONS. YOU BECOME, IN SOME WAYS, SOMETHING SMALLER. LESS *FREE.*

BUT *YOU,* YOU'VE ONLY EVER BEEN LIMITED BY *YOURSELF,* AND YOU'VE NEVER SEEN ANY CEILING AT ALL.

SO YEAH, YOU'LL HEAL. THAT'S NO OBSTACLE FOR THE GREAT TONY STARK. BUT THE *REAL* WOUND--AND I RECALL THIS FROM EXPERIENCE--

--IS KNOWING THAT A *FRIEND* DID THIS TO YOU. SOMEONE YOU *TRUSTED.* SOMEONE YOU *CARED* ABOUT. THAT'S THE PART YOU WON'T SHAKE. THE HUMILIATION AND THE BETRAYAL.

AND THAT'S WHY I WANTED US TO BE ABLE TO SPEAK FREELY-- HONESTLY. SOMETHING I DON'T GET A LOT OF CHANCES TO DO THESE DAYS. BECAUSE THERE ARE THINGS I NEED TO TELL YOU, TRUTHS I NEED TO GET OUT IN THE OPEN.

YOU SEE, I'M NOT THE MAN YOU THINK I AM, TONY--

--BUT I AM STILL WHO I AM. THAT'S THE FIRST TRUTH.

I DON'T KNOW WHEN YOU ALL STARTED TO REALLY LOSE TOUCH--WHEN YOU FORGOT WHO YOU WERE SUPPOSED TO BE FIGHTING FOR--BUT YOU DID.

AND BEFORE YOU KNEW IT, ALL YOUR BIGGEST BATTLES WERE WITH EACH OTHER.

NOW, YOU'D TELL ME THAT'S NOT FAIR. THAT YOU AND DANVERS WERE BOTH ARGUING ABOUT HOW TO MAKE THE WORLD SAFER--THAT YOUR MOTIVES WERE PURE.

YOU'D SAY THAT BECAUSE IT'S THE LIE YOU'VE BEEN TELLING YOURSELF THE ENTIRE TIME.

THE SECOND IS THAT I ALWAYS KNEW THIS WAS GOING TO HAPPEN TO YOU.

NOT BECAUSE I ENGINEERED IT, UNDERSTAND. AND NOT BECAUSE SOMEONE SHOWED ME THE FUTURE--

--BUT BECAUSE THIS WAS *ALWAYS* WHERE YOU WERE GOING TO END UP. ALL OF YOU.

THE FACT IS, THIS WAS ABOUT *AUTHORITY.* YOU WEREN'T WILLING TO PLEDGE FEALTY TO THE FUTURE--BECAUSE THAT WOULD MEAN PLEDGING FEALTY TO SOMETHING BESIDES *YOURSELF.* IT WAS MORE *HUBRIS* THAN *PRINCIPLE.*

AND I KNOW THAT BECAUSE, IN THE *LAST* WAR, YOU HAD NO PROBLEM TELLING ALL OF US TO ACCEPT *YOUR* AUTHORITY.

I GUESS YOU CAN'T REALLY BE BLAMED, THOUGH, CAN YOU? THE SYSTEM YOU LIVE IN IS SO CORRUPT FROM TOP TO BOTTOM IT COULDN'T HELP BUT INFECT YOU.

BUT WHILE YOU WERE BUSY FIGHTING AMONGST YOURSELVES? YOU *MISSED* SOMETHING.

PEOPLE--THE NAMELESS, FACELESS PEOPLE YOU APPOINTED YOURSELVES THE GUARDIANS OF--THEY DECIDED THEY'D HAD *ENOUGH.* THEY WANTED TO FEEL SAFE AND PROTECTED, AND THEY FINALLY REALIZED YOU DON'T ACTUALLY HAVE THE STRENGTH TO GET THEM THERE.

THEY STARTED TO DEMAND SOMETHING BETTER. AND ON THAT FRONT--

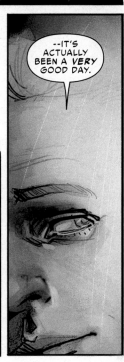

--IT'S ACTUALLY BEEN A *VERY* GOOD DAY.

EARLIER.

--WE NOW GO LIVE TO CAPITOL HILL, WHERE STEVE ROGERS--CAPTAIN AMERICA--IS BEING SWORN IN AS DIRECTOR OF S.H.I.E.L.D.-- IN THE KIND OF GALA CEREMONY USUALLY RESERVED FOR HEADS OF STATE--

THIS WILL BE ROGERS' SECOND STINT AS DIRECTOR OF S.H.I.E.L.D., THE FIRST COMING AFTER THE DISSOLUTION OF H.A.M.M.E.R. AND NORMAN OSBORN'S SIEGE OF ASGARD, WHEN THE WORLD WAS STILL RECOVERING FROM THE EVENTS OF THE FIRST SUPERHUMAN CIVIL WAR.

THIS TENURE IS LIKELY TO BE MARKEDLY DIFFERENT, HOWEVER--

--IN LARGE PART THANKS TO THE NEWLY PASSED S.H.I.E.L.D. ACT, WHICH WAS JUST SIGNED INTO LAW WITH BIPARTISAN SUPPORT IN CONGRESS.

THE ACT DRAMATICALLY EXPANDS S.H.I.E.L.D'S AUTHORITY WITHIN THE UNITED STATES--IN AREAS OF LAW ENFORCEMENT, MASS SURVEILLANCE, AND RESOURCE ALLOCATION-- EVEN ALLOWING THE ORGANIZATION TO BECOME A DE FACTO "TOP COP" IN THE EVENT OF A NATIONAL STATE OF EMERGENCY.

MANY NATIONAL SECURITY EXPERTS WERE QUICK TO SOUND ALARM BELLS.

ANY TIME WE CONSOLIDATE THIS MUCH POWER IN ONE INDIVIDUAL, IT'S ALMOST INEVITABLE THAT WE SEE ABUSE. AND OBVIOUSLY, CAPTAIN AMERICA IS NO ORDINARY MAN, BUT THE PRECEDENT THAT THIS SETS--

THERE'S LITTLE CHANCE OUR CURRENT UNDERSTANDING OF HUMAN RIGHTS AND INTERNATIONAL LAW CAN SURVIVE THIS.

James Green

BUT OTHERS-- LIKE COMMENTATOR HARRY HAUSER-- DISAGREE--

WHAT THIS DOES IS SIMPLE--IT CLEARS OUT THE BUREAUCRACY AND THE CORRUPTION. IT GIVES CONTROL BACK TO THE PEOPLE!

I MEAN, LOOK AT OUR CHOICES IN THIS LAST CIVIL WAR-- A LEFT-COAST TECH BILLIONAIRE AND AN ESTABLISHMENT NEOCON HAWK. PEOPLE ARE TIRED OF BEING RULED BY OUT-OF-TOUCH ELITES WHO ARE ONLY LOOKING TO GAIN MORE INFLUENCE FOR THEMSELVES!

THEY WANT A REAL LEADER, SOMEONE WHO WILL STAND UP FOR THEM-- AND HAS THE POWER TO GET THINGS DONE.

Harry Hauser

AND WITH LOOMING THREATS OF TERRORISM AND INVASION ON THE HORIZON, MANY HEROES WHO SERVE WITH ROGERS WERE QUICK TO SHOW THEIR SUPPORT--

LOOK, IF THIS WAS ANYONE ELSE, I MIGHT BE WORRIED. BUT THIS IS STEVE ROGERS. I TRUST THE MAN WITH MY LIFE.

AND IF HE SAYS THIS IS SOMETHING HE NEEDS, THEN I SAY WE GIVE IT TO HIM. BECAUSE-- LOOKING AROUND AT WHERE WE ARE RIGHT NOW? PRETTY CLEAR TO ME--

--WE NEED CAPTAIN AMERICA MORE THAN EVER.

Sam Wilson

A SENTIMENT ECHOED BY THE HUNDREDS OF THOUSANDS WHO HAVE COME TO SEE HIM SWORN IN.

I--I THINK HE'S GONNA MAKE US SAFE. HE'S GONNA CLEAN UP THIS MESS, AND HE'S GONNA MAKE US PROUD.

WE'RE FINALLY GONNA HAVE SOMEONE IN THERE THAT KNOWS WHAT HE'S DOIN', 'CAUSE GOOD LORD--

Jason Henry

WASP?!

SPIDER-MAN. SPIDER-MAN TWO? I DON'T KNOW WHAT TO CALL YOU NOW THAT I'M WORKING WITH THE OTHER ONE. WHY ARE YOU UP HERE?

GUESS I COULD ASK YOU THE SAME THING--

ME? I'M LATE FOR THE BIG SHOW. DON'T WORRY--I DON'T THINK I'LL HAVE A HARD TIME SNEAKING IN. BUT THEN I SEE SPIDER-MAN TWO UP HERE--

OKAY, YOU CAN STOP CALLING ME THAT.

FINE BY ME. YOU CAN BE SPIDER-MAN ONE. I LIKE YOU BETTER ANYWAY. BUT MY QUESTION--

WHAT AM I DOING HERE? YEAH. WELL, THE REST OF THE CHAMPIONS ARE UP ON STAGE, BUT I FIGURED IT'D BE BETTER IF I HUNG BACK.

WHY?

ARE YOU KIDDING? ME, STEVE ROGERS, CAPITOL BUILDING? YOU KNOW, THE WHOLE VISION THING THAT ULYSSES GUY HAD?

"I'M THE GUY THAT KILLS CAPTAIN AMERICA."

BUT I DON'T UNDERSTAND. THE FIGHT'S *OVER.* YOU *DIDN'T* KILL HIM. FUTURE BOY WAS WRONG.

÷SIGH÷ WHY DOES EVERYBODY THINK THAT? JUST BECAUSE IT DIDN'T HAPPEN *THEN* DOESN'T MEAN IT *WON'T* HAPPEN--

--IT JUST MEANS IT DIDN'T HAPPEN *THAT* DAY.

OH. I SEE. SO WHY DID YOU EVEN COME, THEN? WHY NOT JUST STAY BACK IN NEW YORK OR SOMETHING? WOULDN'T THAT BE SAFER?

I DUNNO...I GUESS I JUST--I WANTED TO AT LEAST BE ABLE TO *HEAR* IT--

BUT WHEN I LOOKED AT THE CHALLENGES BEFORE US--AND THE DEFEATS THAT PRECEDED THEM-- I REALIZED THERE WAS NO DECISION TO BE MADE AT ALL.

THAT NONE OF US COULD AFFORD TO DO LESS THAN EVERYTHING OUR ABILITIES ALLOWED.

AND SO I ACCEPT THIS POSITION WITH A HEAVY HEART, AND A DESIRE TO SEE ITS AUTHORITY AND REACH DIMINISHED THE MOMENT IT IS NO LONGER NEEDED.

UNTIL THAT DAY, THOUGH, I WILL WORK TO HONOR THIS SACRED TRUST THAT YOU HAVE PLACED IN ME-- TO USE THESE POWERS RESPONSIBLY AND IN KEEPING WITH THOSE VALUES WE HOLD SO DEAR.

BECAUSE I BELIEVE THAT'S REALLY WHAT THIS IS ALL ABOUT--

--NOT TO JUST AVOID CATASTROPHE OR DESTRUCTION, BUT TO USE THESE ADVERSITIES TO MAKE OURSELVES SOMETHING STRONGER--

--TO FORGE SOMETHING GREAT FROM THE FIRES THEY WOULD SEE BURN.

THAT'S MY CALL TO ALL OF YOU--TO ASSEMBLE. ASSEMBLE UNDER ONE BANNER--FROM THE AVENGERS TO S.H.I.E.L.D. TO THE UNITED STATES AND OUR ALLIES TO THE WORLD SECURITY COUNCIL AND THE UNITED NATIONS--

--TO EVERY, MAN, WOMAN AND CHILD WHO BELIEVES IN GOOD ON THIS EARTH.

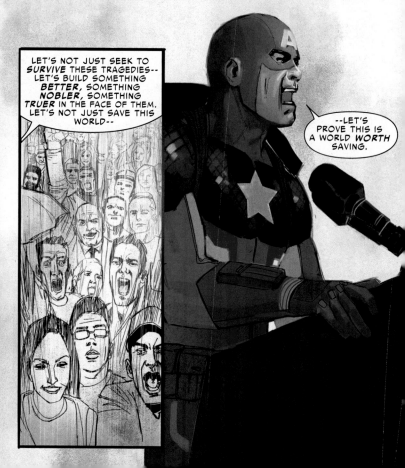

LET'S NOT JUST SEEK TO SURVIVE THESE TRAGEDIES-- LET'S BUILD SOMETHING BETTER, SOMETHING NOBLER, SOMETHING TRUER IN THE FACE OF THEM. LET'S NOT JUST SAVE THIS WORLD--

--LET'S PROVE THIS IS A WORLD WORTH SAVING.

I LIKE TO THINK YOU WOULD'VE BEEN PROUD, TONY.

BUT I DON'T KNOW--YOU PROBABLY WOULD'VE FOUND SOME EXCUSE TO STAND IN MY WAY.

I MEAN, THAT'S YOU, ISN'T IT?

THE FUTURIST. SO IN LOVE WITH HIS OWN VISION OF WHAT'S TO COME THAT HE'D RATHER START A WAR THAN ACCEPT SOMEONE ELSE'S.

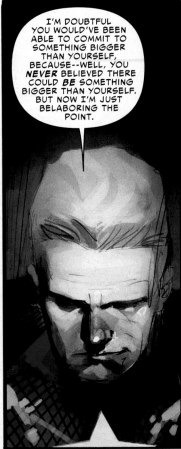

I'M DOUBTFUL YOU WOULD'VE BEEN ABLE TO COMMIT TO SOMETHING BIGGER THAN YOURSELF, BECAUSE--WELL, YOU *NEVER* BELIEVED THERE COULD *BE* SOMETHING BIGGER THAN YOURSELF. BUT NOW I'M JUST BELABORING THE POINT.

STILL--I THINK YOU WOULD'VE AT LEAST BEEN IMPRESSED.

TO SEE PEOPLE UNITED, WORKING TOWARDS A SINGULAR GOAL, BELIEVING THAT THINGS COULD BE BETTER. I KNOW YOU ALWAYS FELT LIKE YOU STRUGGLED TO *INSPIRE* PEOPLE--

--BUT THAT'S BECAUSE YOU COULD NEVER UNDERSTAND THAT IT ISN'T ABOUT *YOU.* NOT ABOUT WHAT YOU CREATED, OR WHAT YOU'VE DONE, OR WHAT YOU'RE *GOING* TO DO.

IT'S ABOUT *THEM.* AND BEST I CAN TELL, YOU NEVER HAD MUCH *USE* FOR THEM. NEVER *THOUGHT* MUCH OF THEM. ALWAYS BELIEVED YOU WERE BETTER. *SMARTER.*

BUT THEY'RE SMARTER THAN YOU THINK, TONY. THEY KNOW WHEN THEY'RE BEING LIED TO--

CHINK!

"--AND THEY KNOW WHO'S *REALLY* ON THEIR SIDE."

CONGRATULATIONS AGAIN, CAPTAIN. PLEASE KNOW THAT YOU HAVE FULL SUPPORT OF THE KINGDOM OF WAKANDA.

I APPRECIATE THAT, T'CHALLA. LET'S DO A ONE-ON-ONE SOON--THERE ARE SOME INTELLIGENCE-SHARING PROPOSALS I WANT TO RUN PAST YOU--

UH-OH--

BETTER HOLD ON TO YOUR WALLET, YOUR HIGHNESS. I'VE SEEN THE BUDGETS.

LOVELY TO SEE YOU, COMMANDER CARTER.

IT IS QUITE A PARTY.

IT SHOULD'VE BEEN YOU UP THERE TODAY, SHARON.

IF IT HAD BEEN ME, THEY WOULD'VE DONE IT IN THE COAT-ROOM OF THE RUSSELL BUILDING. THIS ONLY WORKS BECAUSE IT'S YOU, STEVE--

--YOU'RE WHAT THE WORLD NEEDS RIGHT NOW.

AND I NEED YOU.

SEE? IT ALL WORKS OUT FOR EVERYONE, THEN--

CRASH!

THE HELL WAS THAT?

THERE'S ALWAYS A PRICE AT AN OPEN BAR.

"...IT'S BEEN A BIG WEEK."

THE WHITE HOUSE.
DAYS EARLIER.

WE CALL IT THE PLANETARY DEFENSE SHIELD, MR. PRESIDENT. AN IMPENETRABLE FORCE FIELD DESIGNED TO STOP THE EARTHBOUND FLOW OF EXTRATERRESTRIAL TRAVEL--HOSTILE OR OTHERWISE--IN ITS TRACKS.

COLONEL DANVERS, WHEN YOU SAY "IMPENETRABLE"--

WE NEED TO DO THE FIELD TESTING, BUT ON PAPER, IT LOOKS LIKE GALACTUS HIMSELF COULDN'T BRING THIS THING DOWN, SIR. IT WILL PERFORM AS ADVERTISED.

AND THAT'S IMPORTANT GIVEN WHERE WE ARE RIGHT NOW.

THIS LAST CIVIL WAR STARTED BECAUSE THANOS AND A CELESTIAL WERE ABLE TO JUST SHOW UP AND NOT SEE A SINGLE BIT OF RESISTANCE UNTIL THEY MADE LANDFALL.

AND WE'RE LOOKING AT THIS INCOMING CHITAURI FLEET--WHICH IS THE LARGEST SINGLE ALIEN ARMY TO EVER COME OUR WAY, EVEN BIGGER THAN THE ANNIHILATION WAVE--GETTING CLOSER EVERY DAY. WE NEED TO BE READY, SIR.

HM. IT'S CERTAINLY AN INTRIGUING PROPOSAL. I'LL NEED TO CONSULT WITH CONGRESS, AND STEVE ROGERS--

WITH ALL DUE RESPECT, SIR, I DON'T THINK THAT'S A GOOD IDEA. YOU'RE AWARE OF THE POLITICS AT PLAY HERE--THIS TECHNOLOGY WAS BROUGHT TO ME BY MARIA HILL, THE FORMER DIRECTOR OF S.H.I.E.L.D.

NO ONE ADMIRES STEVE MORE THAN I DO, BUT--I'M CONCERNED HE MIGHT BE A BIT BIASED AGAINST IT.

BUT BEYOND THAT--IF WE'RE GOING TO MOVE FORWARD WITH THIS, I NEED TO HAVE COMPLETE AUTONOMY. I NEED TO KNOW THAT STEVE MIGHT BE THE AUTHORITY DOWN HERE, BUT I'M IN CHARGE UP THERE.

WELL, I...

LOOK, MR. PRESIDENT--THE LAST TIME I WAS HERE YOU ASKED ME WHAT I WANTED TO DO GOING FORWARD. YOU PUT A LOT OF...IMPRESSIVE OPTIONS ON THE TABLE.

AND I TOLD YOU I'D BEEN THINKING ABOUT THE FUTURE. WELL, THIS IS IT--

--THIS IS OUR FUTURE.

ONE WHERE WE CONTROL OUR OWN DESTINY.

I THINK I UNDERSTAND WHY THE TWO OF YOU FOUGHT SO MUCH, TONY--

--SHE'S TURNING OUT TO BE JUST LIKE YOU.

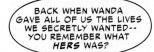

BACK WHEN WANDA GAVE ALL OF US THE LIVES WE SECRETLY WANTED-- YOU REMEMBER WHAT *HERS* WAS?

CAPTAIN MARVEL. THE WORLD'S GREATEST SUPER HERO. LOVED BY EVERYONE. ADORED BY BILLIONS.

I CAN'T HELP BUT FEEL SORRY FOR HER, IN A WAY. TO BE *THAT* DESPERATE FOR APPROVAL, TO HAVE NEVER LEARNED HOW TO FIND IT IN YOURSELF, TO HAVE TO CONSTANTLY SEEK IT OUT IN OTHERS.

IT'S AMAZING HOW IT ALWAYS *BACKFIRES.* HOW THE PEOPLE WHO NEED EVERYONE TO LIKE THEM ALWAYS END UP BEING THE MOST *HATED.*

THE TRUTH IS--AND I THINK YOU'D LOVE TO HEAR IT AND SHE'D NEVER ADMIT IT--SHE LET THIS WAR GET AS BAD AS IT DID FOR ONE SIMPLE REASON--

--SHE COULDN'T STOP TRYING TO PROVE TO HERSELF THAT SHE WAS *BETTER* THAN YOU. COULDN'T STOP FEELING LIKE THE OVERLOOKED SIBLING.

WHICH WOULD BE UNDERSTANDABLE ENOUGH, I SUPPOSE, IF IT WEREN'T FOR ALL THE COLLATERAL DAMAGE.

SHE JUST CAN'T STOP TRYING TO REACH THE TOP OF THAT MOUNTAIN, SO SHE NEVER REALIZES-- THE MORE BODIES SHE STEPS OVER--

"--THE DEEPER THE HOLE SHE DIGS FOR HERSELF."

YOU'RE ANGRY WITH ME.

NO, THAT'S-- THAT'S NOT TRUE--

WHAT WOULD YOU CALL IT, THEN?

DISAPPOINTMENT.

OH, GOD, GIVE ME ANGRY.

CAROL, LOOK AROUND YOU--YOU *WON*. THE PRESIDENT GAVE YOU A MEDAL. PEOPLE ARE *CHEERING* FOR YOU.

YEAH, DOWN THERE, NOT IN HERE.

THAT'S BECAUSE OUR FRIENDS ARE STILL AT EACH OTHER'S THROATS. YOU'VE TOLD THEM TO STOP FIGHTING, BUT YOU HAVEN'T GIVEN THEM A *REASON* TO.

CONSIDER FIGURING OUT HOW TO BRING THEM BACK TOGETHER AGAIN.

STEVE, THE SOFT SELL--YOU KNOW IT'S NOT MY SPECIALTY. IT'S JUST NOT HOW I'M BUILT.

FOR GOOD LEADERS, THERE ARE ALWAYS MORE CONCESSIONS IN *VICTORY* THAN DEFEAT, CAROL.

THEY'LL COME AROUND. ONCE THEY SEE HOW WE GET THINGS DONE, ONCE WE START NOTCHING SOME BIG WINS--THIS WILL ALL TAKE CARE OF ITSELF.

IT WON'T. BUT WHILE WE'RE TALKING ABOUT THE JOB--

UH-OH--

MARIA HILL.

I'VE ALREADY TOLD YOUR GUYS-- I HAVE *NO IDEA* WHERE SHE IS.

YOU REALLY EXPECT ME TO BELIEVE THAT?

IT'S THE TRUTH!

SHE SHOWED UP, GAVE ME THE PLANS FOR THE DEFENSE SHIELD, AND THEN RAN OFF. TO BE TOTALLY HONEST, I WAS PRETTY RELIEVED TO SEE HER GO--

AND YET NOW YOU'RE GOING TO MAKE HER MISTAKES *FOR* HER.

THE SHIELD IS A GOOD IDEA, STEVE.

IT *REALLY* ISN'T. AND IT'S NOT EVEN YOURS--

WELL, TECHNICALLY, HILL FOUND IT IN THE VAULT OF A DECOMMISSIONED VERSION OF YOUR ORGANIZATION, SO LEGALLY IT'S KIND OF A GRAY AREA...

CUTTING US OFF FROM THE REST OF THE UNIVERSE, ISOLATING US--THAT ISN'T A *DEFENSE*, IT'S A *MESSAGE.* YOU KNOW *EXACTLY* WHAT WE'LL BE SAYING TO EVERY LIVING THING ON BOTH SIDES OF IT.

CAP, I DON'T KNOW IF YOU NOTICED, BUT THERE'S *A WAR* COMING. THE CHITAURI FLEET IS GONNA BE IN OUR SOLAR SYSTEM *SOON*--

AND WHEN THEY COME, WE NEED TO BE READY FOR THEM. BUT WE'VE FACED THESE THINGS BEFORE--

THIS ISN'T BEFORE, THOUGH, IS IT?

NO. WE DIDN'T GIVE UP THE THINGS WE BELIEVED IN THOSE TIMES--

THANKS, I CAUGHT YOUR SPEECH.

I--I'M SORRY. IT'S BEEN A LONG MONTH.

NO--IT'S-- IT'S FINE. I DON'T MEAN TO LECTURE.

HEH. LIAR.

IT'S JUST--THIS IS EXACTLY WHAT YOU JUST DID WITH ULYSSES. YOU THINK THERE'S SOME AMOUNT OF EFFECTIVENESS THAT ALLOWS YOU TO DIVORCE A SOLUTION FROM THE *MORALITY* OF IT.

IT DOESN'T WORK THAT WAY, CAROL. IF SOMETHING IS WRONG, IT'S WRONG WHETHER IT SUCCEEDS OR NOT.

WE CAN'T JUST BECOME SLAVES TO ENDS AND MEANS. IT STILL ALL HAS TO STAND FOR SOMETHING, AND IT CAN'T JUST BE *SURVIVING.*

WE'RE *ALL* MAKING COMPROMISES RIGHT NOW--MYSELF INCLUDED. I DON'T ENVY THE DECISION YOU HAVE TO MAKE, BUT I HOPE YOU'LL LISTEN TO ME WHEN I TELL YOU THIS...

THAT SHIELD WILL PUT A CEILING ON THE BEST DREAMS WE'VE EVER HAD. IF YOU BUILD IT, YOU WILL REGRET IT FOR THE REST OF YOUR LIFE.

BUT IT'S YOUR CALL. I CAN'T STOP YOU.

I KNOW YOU'RE GLAD TO FINALLY BE STEERING THE SHIP, CAROL--

--I JUST WISH YOU WOULD WATCH WHERE IT'S HEADED.

STEVE... WAIT--

IT'S TOO LATE FOR HER.

"THEY WERE *AFRAID* WHEN ONE OF THEIR CHILDREN'S CLASSMATES SUDDENLY DEVELOPED THE ABILITY TO INCINERATE ANYONE AROUND THEM WITH A *LOOK*--

"--BUT THEY GOT *ANGRY* WHEN YOU CALLED THEM HYSTERICAL BIGOTS FOR SEEING THAT AS A THREAT TO THEIR SAFETY.

"THEY FELT *AFRAID* WHEN A NEIGHBOR THEY KNEW AND TRUSTED REVEALED THAT ABOVE THEIR COUNTRY AND COMMUNITIES, THEY NOW PLEDGED ALLEGIANCE TO AN ALIEN RACE--A RACE WITH A HISTORY OF *BRUTAL VIOLENCE* AGAINST HUMANITY--

"--BUT THEY GOT *ANGRY* WHEN YOU CALLED THEM INTOLERANT FOR NOT WANTING TO SLEEP NEXT TO THAT.

"YOU SEE, YOU ALL GET TO LIVE IN YOUR SUITS OF ARMOR AND HIDE OUT IN YOUR FORTRESSES--EVEN WHEN YOU *DIE,* YOU GET TO LIVE--

"--BUT THESE ARE *REAL PEOPLE,* TONY. THEY'RE NOT SO LUCKY. AND MAYBE THEY *DON'T* WANT THIS FORWARD-THINKING, FUTURIST UTOPIA YOU'RE BUILDING. MAYBE THEY *DON'T* WANT TO MOVE SO FAR, SO FAST."

THEY MIGHT HAVE EVEN TOLD YOU SO IF YOU EVER BOTHERED TO ASK. IF YOU HADN'T PRETENDED THEY DIDN'T EXIST.

AND THAT'S WHAT MAKES THEM THE ANGRIEST, I IMAGINE. WATCHING YOU FLYING HIGHER AND HIGHER WHILE THEY FEEL THEMSELVES SINKING LOWER AND LOWER.

YOU BUILT GLEAMING TOWERS FULL OF NEW TECHNOLOGIES, OPENED DOORWAYS TO NEW WORLDS--AND THEN YOU LEFT *THEM* BEHIND TO WALLOW IN THE DIRT.

HH. THAT YOU EVER THOUGHT IT WOULD LAST. THAT'S THE *REAL* ARROGANCE OF IT. YOU MADE YOURSELVES *GODS* AND NOW YOU WONDER WHY THE PEOPLE ARE READY TO *CRUCIFY* YOU.

AND *HE* KNEW THAT, TOO.

SEE, THAT'S THE OTHER TRUTH. LIKE I TOLD YOU BEFORE, I'M NOT THE MAN YOU THINK I AM. BUT EVERYTHING *HE* EVER DID, EVERY MEMORY, EVERY MOMENT--I CARRY IT INSIDE ME.

I KNOW EVERY THOUGHT HE EVER HAD ABOUT *YOU*, FOR INSTANCE.

HE LOVED YOU.

HE LOVED YOU, AND HE ADMIRED YOU. EVEN WHEN YOU FOUGHT.

ALL THOSE TIMES YOU THOUGHT YOU OUTSMARTED HIM? THOSE TIMES YOU THOUGHT YOU BEAT HIM?

HE *HAD* YOU. EVERY SINGLE TIME. HE COULD'VE BEATEN YOU, AND HE CHOSE INSTEAD TO GO EASY ON YOU, TO *SPARE* YOU.

YOU'D PROBABLY SMILE AND SAY THAT MADE HIM THE BETTER MAN--

--BUT I'D SAY IT MADE HIM *WEAK*. BECAUSE HE KNEW HOW ALL THIS WOULD END AS WELL, AND HE DIDN'T HAVE THE STRENGTH TO DO WHAT WAS NECESSARY.

HE WAS INFECTED BY THIS... *MIRAGE*.

I'M NOT LIKE THAT, THOUGH. I AM READY TO DO WHAT MUST BE DONE. WE'RE SO VERY CLOSE NOW TO SETTING THINGS RIGHT--AND I JUST CAN'T HELP MYSELF--

--FUNNY ENOUGH, IT MAKES *ME* ANGRY, TOO.

I'M ANGRY THAT YOU'RE NOT HERE FOR THIS. IN FACT, I'M HOPING--*PRAYING*--THAT YOU CAN SOMEHOW HEAR ME AND THIS PULLS YOU OUT OF YOUR SLEEP.

BECAUSE I WANT YOU TO SEE THIS, TONY. MORE THAN ANYTHING--I *NEED* YOU TO SEE WHAT I DO NEXT.

I AM GOING TO *DESTROY EVERYTHING YOU EVER BUILT.*

I AM GOING TO TEAR DOWN THESE INSTITUTIONS THAT YOU'VE USED TO GIVE YOURSELVES POWER. I'M GOING TO REDUCE ALL THAT YOU WORKED FOR, ALL YOU *BLED* FOR, TO A PILE OF RUBBLE AND ASH--

--AND FROM IT I AM GOING TO MAKE SOMETHING BETTER. I AM GOING TO MAKE THIS A *STRONGER* WORLD, ONE FORGED FROM *FIRE.*

SO, PLEASE--I'M BEGGING YOU--WAKE UP NOW. COME AND TRY TO STOP ME.

BUT YOU WON'T. OR YOU CAN'T. DO YOU KNOW HOW I KNOW? BECAUSE THE BOY--ULYSSES--HE SHOWED ME THE FUTURE.

HE EVEN SHOWED IT TO ALL OF YOU AS WELL, BUT, AS USUAL, YOU WERE TOO BLIND TO SEE WHAT REALLY MATTERS.

I WASN'T, THOUGH. IT WAS SOMETHING I'D CARRIED IN MY OWN DREAMS FOR A LIFETIME. AND WHEN I FOUND MYSELF THERE, *FINALLY,* THANKS TO HIM--

--I TOOK IN EVERYTHING AROUND ME. I LET MY EYES OPEN, AND I FELT THE VISION TAKE ME. LET IT REVEAL THE TRUTH TO ME AND ME ALONE. UNTIL NOW.

DO YOU WANT TO KNOW WHAT I SAW, TONY?

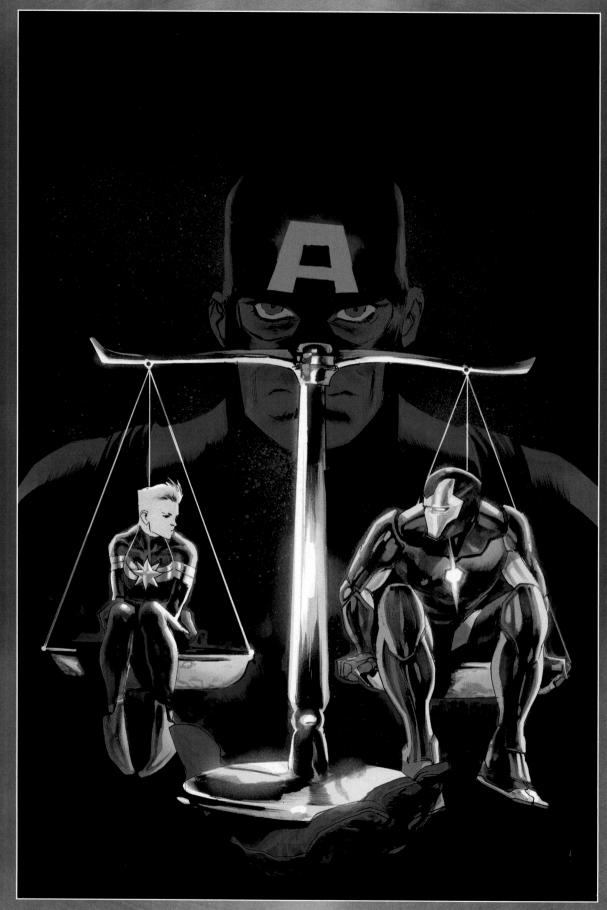

Civil War II: The Oath variant by
RAFAEL ALBUQUERQUE

Steve ★ Rogers
CAPTAIN AMERICA

Steve Rogers' reality has been secretly rewritten by Kobik, a sentient Cosmic Cube acting under the influence of the Red Skull. In Steve's new history, a Hydra agent named Elisa Sinclair enrolled Steve in a school where he was trained to believe in Hydra's ideals – and befriended a young Helmut Zemo. The leaders of Hydra recognized Steve's promise and gave him a secret mission: return to the U.S. to become the first Super-Soldier – and consequently, Hydra's ultimate spy.

In the present, Steve has gained a powerful ally by convincing Zemo that the version of history where they were friends really took place, and that the version Zemo remembered was a lie. But his number of enemies is growing as well--after being replaced by Steve as the Director of S.H.I.E.L.D., Maria Hill is on the run, while his friend Bucky Barnes is still hiding out with Kobik, who could reveal Steve's secret at any time. And Taskmaster and Black Ant just stumbled across security footage of Captain America saying "Hail Hydra"...

ALONGSIDE HIS BEST PAL, *BUCKY,* HE'S BRINGING **HOPE** TO OUR BOYS--

--AND GIVING **HELL** TO THE *NAZI SCUM!*

TOGETHER THEY'RE LEADING THE CHARGE AGAINST THE *REICH*--

--AND THEIR ALLIES IN THE EVIL ORGANIZATION KNOWN AS *HYDRA!*

WHOSE **BARON HEINRICH ZEMO** LEADS AN ARMY OF TERROR--

--AND DEVELOPS AN ENTIRE ENEMY SUPER-SOLDIER SQUADRON OF HIS OWN!

NOT JUST THAT-- BUT IN GERMANY, WHISPERS OF A NEW PLAYER--A VICIOUS MADMAN KNOWN AS THE **RED SKULL**-- HAVE EMERGED, BREATHING NEW LIFE INTO THE AXIS EFFORT!

BUT NEVER FEAR, DEAR VIEWER--WE'LL ALWAYS COME OUT AHEAD IN THE END--

--NOW THAT WE HAVE **CAPTAIN AMERICA** ON OUR SIDE!

NOW.

From the journal of Doctor Erik Selvig:

These last few months have been quite the whirlwind.

My job once had been watching after Kobik--the living embodiment of the Cosmic Cube--supposedly on behalf of S.H.I.E.L.D.

But in truth I served the Red Skull and Hydra--until he tired of me and ordered my death, that is--

--at which point I came to serve someone new.

I have grown to admire this man who saved me, and I believe in what he is trying to do for the glory of Hydra--

--but even he makes mistakes sometimes.

AH, THERE HE IS. DOCTOR SELVIG--

CAPTAIN...

AS YOU CAN SEE, WE HAVE A NEW ALLY. **HELMUT ZEMO** HAS AGREED TO JOIN OUR CAUSE--AND I COULD NOT BE MORE PROUD.

NOW, I HAVE TO GO DEAL WITH SOME **S.H.I.E.L.D.** BUSINESS--BUT I WANT YOU TO ASSIST HIM IN ANY WAY HE DEEMS NECESSARY. WE HAVE A LOT TO GET DONE, AND VERY LITTLE TIME IN WHICH TO ACCOMPLISH IT.

THANK YOU, STEVEN. AND DOCTOR, BEFORE WE BEGIN, I'D LIKE TO **APOLOGIZE** FOR ALL THAT EARLIER UNPLEASANTNESS--

DO YOU MEAN DRAGGING ME THROUGH THE HIMALAYAS ON A LEASH AS YOUR PRISONER? OR PLANNING TO KILL ME AFTER YOU UNCOVERED ALL THE SECRETS OF THE COSMIC CUBE?

CAN WE SAY **BOTH?**

CAPTAIN, YOU CANNOT EXPECT ME TO WORK WITH THIS MAN!

I **CAN** AND I **DO**, DOCTOR. WHATEVER DIFFERENCES THE TWO OF YOU MAY HAVE HAD BEFORE, IT'S TIME TO PUT THEM ASIDE.

WE ARE ON THE **SAME TEAM** NOW. AND IT'S WE FEW AGAINST THE MANY. SO, DOCTOR, I EXPECT YOU TO PUT YOUR LOYALTY TO HYDRA ABOVE YOUR OWN PERSONAL GRIEVANCES.

AND **YOU,** HELMUT. I UNDERSTAND THE DOCTOR MAY TAKE SOME TIME TO COME AROUND, AND THAT MAY COME TO FRUSTRATE YOU, BUT, NO MATTER HOW MUCH YOU MAY WANT TO--

--DO NOT VAPORIZE HIM WHILE I'M GONE.

HMPH.

DIRECTOR ON DECK!

GONNA TAKE A LITTLE WHILE TO GET USED TO THAT AGAIN. AT EASE, PEOPLE--

--WHAT DO WE HAVE?

YOU'RE GONNA LOVE THIS ONE--SHOWED UP AT THE **MUSEUM OF AMERICAN HISTORY** AND STARTED WRECKING THE PLACE...

"...OUR OLD PAL, THE **AWESOME ANDROID.**"

SO, THE **MAD THINKER?**

NOT THIS TIME, CAP--BEST I CAN TELL IT'S BEEN REMOTELY **HACKED,** CAN'T SAY BY WHO--BUT THEY'RE USING A REALLY SOPHISTICATED VIRUS THAT'S BEEN FLOATING AROUND ATTACKING A.I.

LAST MONTH IT INFECTED A FLEET OF **DOOMBOTS,** MADE THEM ALL TWERK IN **TRAFALGAR SQUARE.** THINK IT WAS AN ANTI-GLOBALISM THING.

WE'VE GOT A TEAM OF **HULKBUSTERS** EN ROUTE, ETA 12 MINUTES.

THAT'S TOO LONG--

THIS THING WAS NOT SUPPOSED TO BE IN MY WAY--

WASN'T

PART

OF

THE PLAN.

AND I'LL ADMIT I'M STRUGGLING TO ADJUST.

HURRY, CLOSE THE DOOR. YOU'RE SURE THAT BRAT *BUCKY* DIDN'T SEE YOU? IT WOULD BE A SHAME IF WE HAD TO *ELIMINATE* HIM--

STOP IT, HELMUT--

--BUCKY'S A GOOD KID. HE'S JUST BEEN...*BRAINWASHED.* LIKE ALL THE *REST* OF THEM. BUT HE SHOULD GET THE CHANCE TO RENOUNCE ALL THAT--

--ONCE WE WIN THIS WAR.

HM-- AND ON THAT FRONT--

HERE IT IS. TROOP DEPLOYMENTS, NEW SUPPLY ROUTES--AND EVERYTHING I COULD GET ON THE ALLIES' NEW SUPER-WEAPON.

STEVEN, YOU--YOU ARE *INCREDIBLE!* HOW DO YOU MANAGE TO *GET* ALL THIS--?

THEIR LEADERSHIP IS SO CORRUPT, SO PETTY--THEY'LL PUT THEIR TRUST IN JUST ABOUT *ANYONE* WHO ISN'T STAINED BY THEIR COWARDICE.

BUT NONE OF IT WILL MATTER IF WE DON'T HAVE AN ANSWER FOR ALL THIS--HOW IS ZOLA'S *SUPER-SOLDIER PROGRAM* COMING ALONG?

FOR A MAN WHO DIED OF A HEART ATTACK IN AMERICAN CUSTODY, BETTER THAN COULD BE EXPECTED, I SUPPOSE--

--BUT STILL *SLOW.* HE WON'T ADMIT IT, BUT HE'S STRUGGLING TO REPLICATE ERSKINE'S FORMULA ON ANYONE BESIDES YOU. THE NEW SOLDIERS ARE MORE LIMITED, MORE AGGRESSIVE--AND THEY HAVE A BAD HABIT OF DYING ON THE TABLE.

HOW MANY ACTIVE?

STILL FEWER THAN A *DOZEN.*

DAMN IT-- YOU NEED TO GET ME OUT OF HERE, HELMUT-- GET ME FIGHTING ON THE RIGHT SIDE OF THIS THING--

NO, STEVEN-- YOU ARE *ALREADY* THE BEST WEAPON WE HAVE, RIGHT WHERE YOU ARE. OF COURSE, THAT MAY CHANGE SOON...

WHAT DO YOU MEAN?

I WANTED TO TELL YOU IN PERSON-- I AM GOING AWAY FOR A BIT TO HELP MY FATHER ON A VERY IMPORTANT MISSION, SECURING A PIECE OF EXPERIMENTAL TECHNOLOGY THE BRITISH HAVE BEEN DEVELOPING--

"--ONE THAT COULD TURN THE TIDE OF THIS WAR."

BUT BEFORE I GO--I HAVE A *MISSION* FOR YOU AS WELL, OLD FRIEND. ONE I AM QUITE UNSURE HOW YOU WILL FEEL ABOUT--

I DON'T UNDERSTAND.

...ELISA?

SO, YES, SURPRISES--

IT TURNS OUT YOU ARE NOT THE *ONLY* WOLF IN SHEEP'S CLOTHING. HYDRA HAS A SPY OF OUR OWN IN ITS MIDST.

AND IT IS SOMEONE WE *BOTH KNOW* QUITE WELL--IN FACT, SHE IS THE ONE WHO BROUGHT YOU TO US IN THE FIRST PLACE-- THE WITCH.

STILL NOT IN LOVE WITH THEM.

FOOM!

S.H.I.E.L.D. COMMAND--THIS IS THE *DIRECTOR*. TARGET NEUTRALIZED--

--BUT I'M PRETTY SURE HE JUST TRASHED MY OWN DISPLAY.

Now, I must admit--

--Zemo's new attitude confuses me.

For weeks, Captain Rogers has been trying to get through to him--

--telling him stories about another life, where they were the closest of friends.

This itself is not strange.

In Pleasant Hill, all of the prisoners had their reality rewritten by Kobik-- but the effects were isolated to themselves.

What if Kobik did something different this time?

Something more profound?

That might explain why a zealot like Zemo is predisposed to believe in the Captain's tale--

--but what else could it mean for this world? For reality itself?

What new truths might emerge?

UNBELIEVABLE. MAKE ME WAIT A **WHOLE DAMNED HOUR?** AFTER I PULL ALL THIS TOGETHER FOR YOU? POOR **CUSTOMER SERVICE,** TASKMASTER--

--THIS IS WHY PEOPLE **OUTSOURCE.**

HEY--WAIT-- FRRRR--THAT'S OUR--NN--MONEY! I WAS GONNA BUY AN **APPLE WATCH!**

IS THAT ALL YOU CARE FOR? **MONEY?**

I WOULD HAVE YOU DREAM OF GREATER THINGS.

NN-- LIKE THE **GOLD** APPLE WATCH?

YOU'VE INTERFERED IN SOMETHING FAR LARGER THAN YOURSELVES TODAY, THE BOTH OF YOU. MOST MEN WHO FIND THEMSELVES STANDING BETWEEN ME AND MY PLANS ARE REDUCED TO THE DUST FROM WHENCE THEY CAME--

--BUT I **LIKE** YOU TWO. YOU'RE **FUNNY.** AND I THINK YOU CAN BE OF SOME USE TO ME.

HHHRR-- YEAH? AND WHO THE HELL ARE **YOU,** LADY?!

HM. I THOUGHT THE SUIT WOULD BE **FAMILIAR** TO YOU--

--I AM MADAME HYDRA.

BUT SINCE WE ARE GOING TO BE WORKING TOGETHER SO CLOSELY FROM NOW ON, GENTLEMEN--

--YOU MAY CALL ME ELISA. ELISA SINCLAIR.

HOW'S HE DOING IT? THERE'S **TEN** OF US!

I TOLD YA-- WE SHOULDA BET **TWENTY** GUYS.

BETTER LUCK NEXT TIME, FELLAS. SEE YOU ON THE FRONT LINES!

I THOUGHT THE GUY WAS SUPPOSED TO BE VISITING FOR A MORALE BOOST...

QUITE A **COMMOTION** IN HERE--

IT'S OUR **BIG BREAK**, CAPTAIN. APPARENTLY HYDRA'S GOT SOMEONE ON THE INSIDE WHO FEELS LIKE TALKING. SENT US A CODED MESSAGE OVER THE WIRES.

WHAT'S THE INTEL?

YOU'RE NOT GONNA BELIEVE THIS. TURNS OUT BARON ZEMO IS RIGHT HERE IN ENGLAND--IN **LONDON**. HE'S LOOKING TO TRY AND STEAL THE DRONE ROCKET THEY'RE BUILDING AT GREENWICH OBSERVATORY.

BUT NOW THAT WE KNOW HE'S COMING, WE'RE FINALLY GONNA CATCH THE MEAN OLD BASTARD, **AND** HIS SON--

...CAP?

...and how it changed everything.

NEW JERSEY. NOW.

I MISS YOU, TOO. SO HOW IS SHE?

OH, DEAR. WELL, *OF COURSE* SHE DRIVES YOU CRAZY. SHE'S YOUR *MOTHER.* BUT IT'S GOOD THAT YOU GET TO VISIT ANYWAY--

DING DONG

OH, HONEY--I HAVE TO GO, THERE'S SOMEONE AT THE DOOR.

WHAT? NO, I DIDN'T ORDER A PIZZA. *YES,* I SAW THE KALE SALAD IN THE REFRIGERATOR. GIVE MY LOVE TO THE GIRLS. TELL THEM I--

--MISS THEM.

GOOD EVENING, NEIGHBOR--

--MIGHT I BORROW SOME SUGAR?

"--WHEN THE BOMB DROPS."

SOKOVIA.
NOW.

OUR FORCES ARE MAKING GOOD PROGRESS, FATHER-- WE EXPECT TO HAVE THE TOWN TAKEN BY NIGHTFALL.

MOST *ENCOURAGING,* SIN--BUT THE TOWN IS *NOT* OUR OBJECTIVE TODAY--

BOOM!

THIS IS.

ARE THOSE--?

YES, SIN, THEY *ARE.*

THE KEY TO OUR VICTORY IN THE WAR AGAINST S.H.I.E.L.D.

I DON'T UNDERSTAND-- THIS PLACE WASN'T EVEN GUARDED.

THAT'S BECAUSE NO ONE EVEN *KNEW* THEY WERE HERE...

WHEN THE SOVIET UNION FELL AND SOKOVIA BECAME INDEPENDENT, GENERAL NOVOTY USED THE WEAPONS THE RUSSIANS HAD LEFT BEHIND AS LEVERAGE.

SO LONG AS HE AGREED TO THE DISARMAMENT TREATY, THE WESTERN POWERS TURNED A BLIND EYE TO HIS... ECCENTRICITIES...

BUT THE TRUTH IS EVEN *HE* HAD NO IDEA WHERE ALL THE WEAPONS WERE. BECAUSE, LOATH AS THE WORLD IS TO ACCEPT THE REALITY, WE HAVE ACTUALLY BEEN QUITE *CARELESS* WITH OUR WEAPONS OF MASS DESTRUCTION.

THAT'S WHAT DESTROYED THE *RED EMPIRE,* YOU KNOW--

--POOR BOOKKEEPING.

EARLIER.

DOCTOR SELVIG-- WHERE IS STEVEN?

ER-- CALLED AWAY ON S.H.I.E.L.D. BUSINESS, I'M AFRAID.

GOOD.

"GOOD"? OH-- YOU'RE NOT GOING TO TRY TO *KILL* ME AGAIN...

-*SIGH*- NO. THERE IS SOMETHING I WANT TO *DISCUSS* WITH YOU.

EXPANSION.

AS STEVEN'S PLAN COMES CLOSER TO FRUITION, HE WILL NEED MORE RESOURCES THAN WE TWO ALONE CAN PROVIDE.

I SEE-- AND YOU'VE DISCUSSED THIS WITH HIM?

IT IS A... SURPRISE?

HH. WELL, ACTUALLY, ON THIS POINT, WE *AGREE.* AND I MIGHT HAVE JUST THE SOLUTION.

YOU SEE, WHEN I OVERSAW THE PLEASANT HILL PROGRAM, AS NEW INMATES WERE ADMITTED, I ADMINISTERED A TRACKING CHIP. S.H.I.E.L.D. BELIEVED IT WAS FOR THEIR BENEFIT, BUT IN TRUTH--IT WAS A RESOURCE FOR HYDRA.

VERY INTERESTING. WHICH INMATES?

YOU MEAN WITH THE EXCEPTION OF THE ONES WHO ESCAPED WITH KOBIK?

ALL OF THEM.

I have known you for a lifetime, Helmut.

I have marveled at your perseverance--

--your commitment to our cause.

You gave up so much--

--and still the world demanded more.

Still it took so much from you.

I LOVE YOU, MY SON.

Still it made you suffer.

CAP, GET BACK!

BUCKY! WHAT--WHAT HAVE YOU DONE?!

DON'T WORRY, CAP-- I CAN ALTER THE TRAJECTORY OF THE ROCKET FROM HERE-- SO THAT INSTEAD OF THE BIG APPLE, IT TOUCHES DOWN IN THE MIDDLE OF THE ATLANTIC!

WE'LL SEND ZEMO STRAIGHT INTO THE OCEAN WHERE HE BELONGS!

"--YOU AND MANY OTHERS."

It was my failure that day that cost your father his life, Helmut--

--and I have never stopped trying to earn your forgiveness since then. But now, I can offer you something else.

Now I can begin to make things right.

I will give you the revenge you so richly deserve.

You will lead an army.

And together--

--we will change the world.

13 Venomized variant by
TOM RANEY & CHRIS SOTOMAYOR

14

1944.

IT IS A WONDROUS THING TO SEE YOUR DREAMS REALIZED.

AND YOU WERE ALWAYS MY MOST CHERISHED DREAM, DEAR CHILD.

TO SEE THAT SCARED LITTLE BOY GROW INTO A MAN--

--ONE WHO EMBODIES STRENGTH AND CONVICTION TO HIS VERY CORE...

...THAT FILLS MY HEART WITH PRIDE.

BUT TIME AND DISTANCE ARE STRANGE THINGS--

--AND THEY HAVE A WAY OF KEEPING US FROM WHAT WE LOVE.

OH MY-- I DON'T BELIEVE IT...

...STEVEN?

ELISA?

STEVEN! IT'S REALLY YOU!

HAVE YOU COME TO KILL ME, THEN?

OH, HOW I HAVE MISSED YOU, MY SWEET BOY. BUT I KNOW--

@#!$!

GAH! THIS IS WORSE THAN THAT TIME I GOT BEDBUGS! AND THE SECOND TIME I GOT BEDBUGS!

OH, I GET IT--IT'S LIKE A PUZZLE--A SLIMY, CREEPY, WORMY PUZZLE. S'GROSS.

ZISTM ZE ZCIEGSEEIZE

÷SNIFF SNIFF÷ HELLO, PRETTY MONSTER.

MY HIVE.

I OFFER YOU VIOLENCE.

MADRIPOOR.

FIRE!!!

TAKE THE HEADS, STRING THE BODIES ALONG THE PIER. LET EVERYONE SEE WHAT HAPPENS WHEN THEY TRY TO MOVE *THEIR* PRODUCT INTO *MY* TERRITORY.

-:SIGH:- IS THIS ALL YOU ARE TO BE, THEN?

THE DEADLY VIPER--ONCE THE SUPREME HYDRA--NOW DIRTIES HERSELF IN THESE SLUMS, SLINGING OPIATES LIKE SOME LOWLY CRIMINAL...

IT'S ENOUGH TO BREAK A GIRL'S HEART.

THAT'S MY SUIT YOU'RE WEARING.

HH. WELL, PERHAPS YOU COULD TRY TO TAKE IT BACK FROM ME, DARLING--

--SHOW ME WHAT THE MAN I LOVED SAW IN YOU ALL THOSE YEARS AGO.

WHO ARE YOU?

SOMEONE WHO SEES YOU HAVE DRIFTED FOR TOO LONG, LITTLE ORPHAN CHILD--

--I OFFER YOU *BELONGING.*

--AND SO YEAH, I'M THINKING ABOUT MAJORING IN PSYCHOLOGY, SURE-- BUT I DUNNO--IT'S NOT REALLY VERY *GLAMOROUS*, IS IT?

MOMMY SAYS I DON'T EVEN *NEED* TO GO TO SCHOOL ANYMORE, NOW THAT SHE'S REMARRIED. AND I WAS THINKING ABOUT MAYBE JUST GOING FULL-TIME ON BUILDING MY *INSTAGRAM BRAND*--

HMM. YES. WELL, HAVE A SEAT, MEGHAN, DEAR-- PERHAPS I CAN HELP YOUR MIND REACH THE CLARITY IT NEEDS--AND WE CAN DISCUSS THE PLANS FOR YOUR *INHERITANCE* A BIT MORE, AS WELL--

UGH--

--JUST LIKE YOUR *FATHER*. HE WAS A MAN OF LOW AIMS AND AMBITIONS, AS WELL.

WE RARELY SAW EYE TO EYE.

WHAT THE DEVIL--?!

BUT I MUST ADMIT, HE *DID* HAVE HIS USES.

DOCTOR FAUSTUS, WHO *IS* THIS?! YOU SAID I WAS THE ONLY--

FAUSTUS. MY DEAR, YOU EVEN HAVE HIS TASTE FOR MELODRAMA.

YOU WILL LEAVE NOW. YOU WILL *LEAVE*--

YOUR PARLOR TRICKS WON'T WORK ON ME, JOHANN. NOR SHOULD YOU WANT THEM TO. AFTER ALL, I COME WITH A GIFT--THE THING YOU'VE CRAVED THE MOST THROUGHOUT YOUR FRUSTRATED, INSIGNIFICANT LIFE...

I OFFER YOU *INFLUENCE*.

I WILL ADMIT--THIS ISN'T EASY FOR ME.

THE MAN THIS SUIT BELONGED TO--HE MEANT A GREAT DEAL TO ME. BUT, CUT OFF ONE LIMB--

WELL, THE POINT IS I BELIEVE THERE IS VALUE IN LEGACY. IT WAS JUST A QUESTION OF FINDING A SUITABLE HEIR--

--AND YOU *ARE* FAMILY, AFTER ALL.

I SEE--

--AND DOES...*HE* KNOW?

NO. AND HE NEVER WILL. HE BELIEVES YOU TO BE DEAD, AND SO THAT IS THE TRUTH OF IT. WHOEVER YOU WERE BEFORE, HE *PERISHED* LONG BEFORE THIS--

YOU ARE THE *KRAKEN* NOW. THE GHOST OF WORLDS LOST, THE KEEPER OF SECRETS--

I OFFER YOU *MEANING.*

YES, WE WILL BE TOGETHER AGAIN, STEVEN. AND WHEN I SEE YOU, I WILL BRING WITH ME A GIFT...

...THE NEW
HIGH COUNCIL
OF HYDRA.

"ALL RIGHT, ALPHA FLIGHT, LOOK ALIVE--THE EYES OF THE WORLD ARE UPON US."

I AM HEREBY AUTHORIZING A GO COMMAND ON THE FIRST OFFICIAL TEST OF OUR PRIDE AND JOY--

"--THE PLANETARY DEFENSE SHIELD."

SHIELD IS ONLINE AND OPERATIONAL MA'AM.

GOOD. LET'S GET STARTED, THEN--

MA'AM-- THE DIRECTOR OF S.H.I.E.L.D. IS REQUESTING TO COME ON BOARD--

TELL MARIA--

OH, RIGHT. I SHOULD BE SO LUCKY.

CAROL--

COLONEL DANVERS.

DIRECTOR-SLASH-CAPTAIN ROGERS. GLAD YOU GOT THE *EVITE*. I ASSUME YOU'RE HERE TO SEE SOME HISTORY GET MADE?

MAYBE--

"--OR MAYBE I JUST WANTED TO TRY TO TALK YOU OUT OF THIS ONE LAST TIME--

"--AFTER OUR *LAST* MEETING DIDN'T GO AS WELL AS I'D HOPED."

STEVE--I UNDERSTAND YOUR CONCERNS. REALLY, I DO. AND IF I FELT WE COULD *AFFORD* TO BE IDEALISTIC AT THIS MOMENT, I'D *LISTEN* TO THEM.

BUT EVERY DAY THE CHITAURI HORDE WIPES OUT ANOTHER SYSTEM ON THEIR WAY TOWARDS US--THIS SHIELD IS OUR ONLY ANSWER.

THIS IS WHAT THE WORLD *NEEDS* RIGHT NOW. AN END TO ALL THIS CRAZINESS. *REAL* STABILITY, WHERE PEOPLE CAN GET ON WITH THEIR LIVES WITHOUT WORRYING ABOUT THE NEXT INVASION OR ATTACK. IMAGINE THAT.

SO EVEN IF YOU'RE NOT THRILLED ABOUT IT, I'M GLAD YOU'RE HERE--THIS WAY, WE GET TO SEE WHAT PEACE LOOKS LIKE, TOGETHER. NOW--

--LAUNCH THE NUKES!

"WE HAVE IMPACT--

"--SHIELD AT 99 PERCENT."

THIRTY NUCLEAR WARHEADS-- 99 PERCENT. NICE--

--BUT LET'S BRING THE *BIG GUNS.*

MONICA-- YOUR TEAM SET?

ON YOUR MARK, CAR.

FULL POWER THEN--

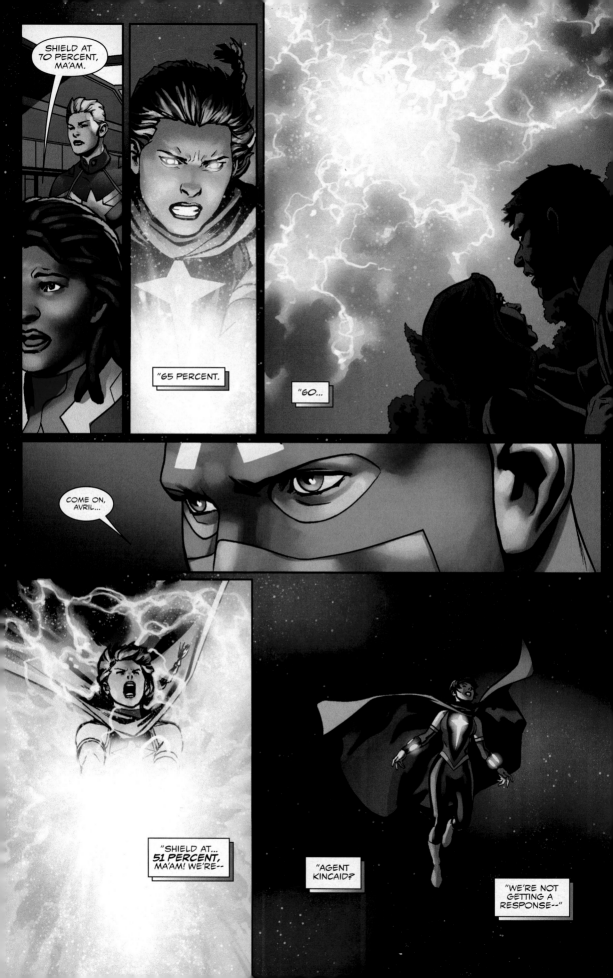

I'M SORRY I LET YOU DOWN, SIR.

YOU GAVE IT EVERYTHING YOU HAD, AGENT. SO YOU DIDN'T.

BUT THE SHIELD--

YOU LET *ME* WORRY ABOUT IT--

"--THERE ARE *OTHER* WAYS TO DEAL WITH THAT."

RICK JONES.

≤SKRRZZT≥ HEY, CAP--

AH, BEFORE WE START, REAL FAST--"OBI-WAN KENOBI, YEARS AGO, YOU SERVED MY FATHER--"

RICK.

NO, SURE, OKAY. WHAT CAN I DO YOU FOR?

YOU REMEMBER HOW I SAID I HAVE A MISSION FOR YOU? WELL, THIS IS IT--YOU LOOKED AT THE *CYBERSECURITY* ON THIS SHIELD?

I DID, AND I GOTTA TELL YOU--THIS IS NO MARIA HILL PRODUCTION. THEY'VE LOCKED IT DOWN NICE AND TIGHT.

I SEE. BUT YOU CAN GET THROUGH IT?

WELL, YEAH, IF PUSH CAME TO SHOVE--

IT'S A SHOVE. CAN YOU DO THIS FOR ME? I'M AFRAID CAPTAIN MARVEL IS MAKING THE SAME MISTAKES SHE MADE DURING THE CIVIL WAR. I CAN'T LET THAT HAPPEN AGAIN. ONE WAY OR ANOTHER, YOU AND I, RICK--

--WE HAVE TO MAKE SURE THAT SHIELD *NEVER* GOES UP--

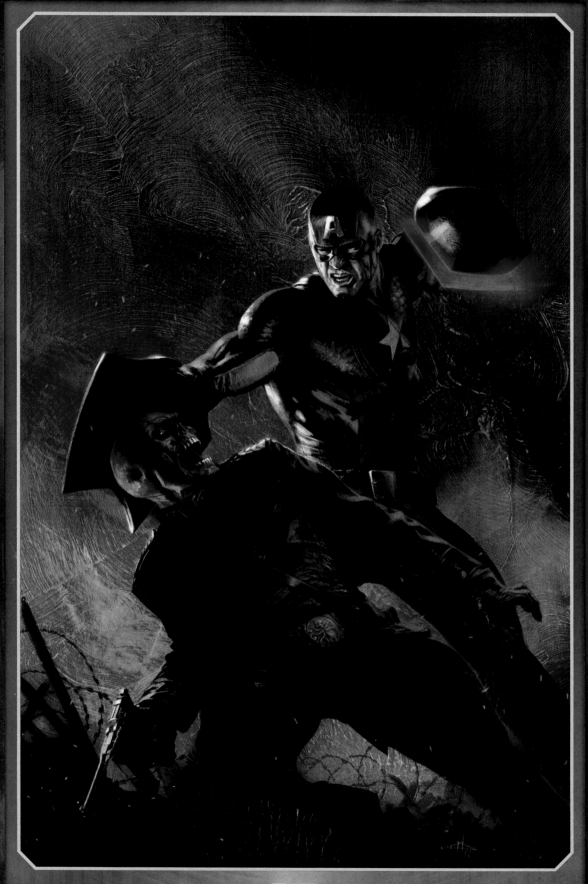

15

I HAVE WAITED SO LONG FOR THIS, SKULL.

TO WATCH YOUR OWN PLAN BECOME YOUR *UNDOING*.

YOU BELIEVED YOU HAD MADE ME YOUR *PERFECT SOLDIER*.

THAT THROUGH THE POWER OF THE COSMIC CUBE, YOU HAD CHANGED WHO I AM.

BUT IN REALITY, YOU ONLY REVEALED MY *TRUE* SELF...

...THOUGH THE KNOWLEDGE OF THAT ALONE WAS NOT ENOUGH TO DEFEAT YOU.

YOU POSSESSED THE BRAIN OF CHARLES XAVIER, MAKING YOU THE WORLD'S MOST POWERFUL TELEPATH--

--WHICH MEANT I COULD NEVER GET CLOSE ENOUGH TO ACT AGAINST YOU--FOR FEAR THAT MY OWN THOUGHTS WOULD BETRAY ME--

--SO I FOUND OTHERS TO DO IT FOR ME.

A TEAM OF AVENGERS, X-MEN AND INHUMANS WHO COULD BE LED TO BELIEVE THAT THEY THEMSELVES HAD THE IDEA TO BRING YOU DOWN--

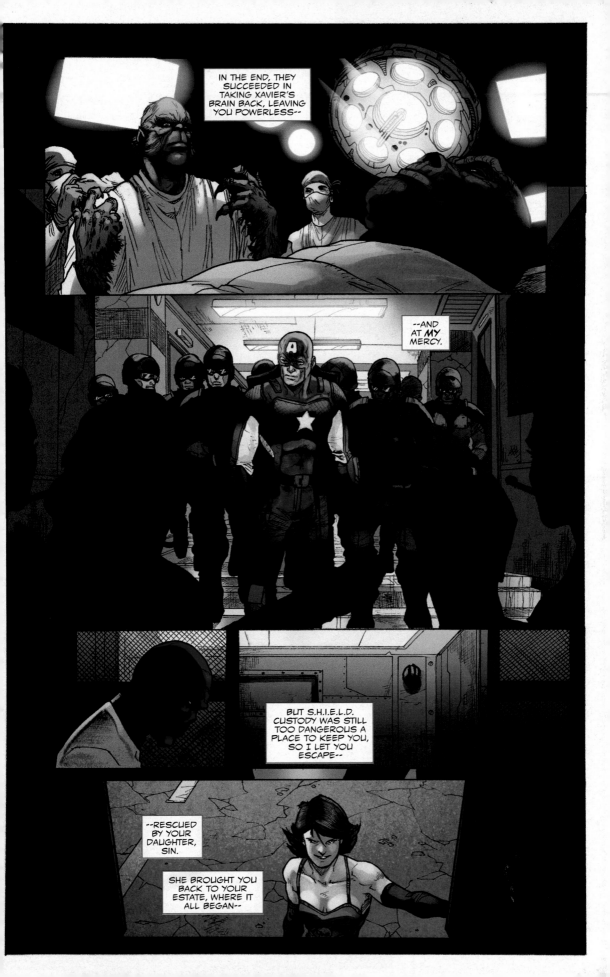

DIRECTOR ROGERS--HAILING, ALL FREQUENCIES-- DIRECTOR ROGERS, PLEASE REPORT IN--

STILL NO RESPONSE, MA'AM.

COME ON, STEVE--WHERE ARE YOU?

COMMANDER--

--SHOULD WE KEEP WAITING?

÷SIGH÷ NO. HE WOULD WANT US TO GO AHEAD. PROCEED.

YES, MA'AM--

"AT 0400 HOURS, THE CAPITAL CITY OF SOKOVIA WAS OVERRUN, AND THE GOVERNMENT AND REBEL FORCES BOTH ISSUED FORMAL SURRENDERS TO HYDRA.

"WE'RE TRYING TO VERIFY THE STATUS OF GENERAL NOVOTY--

"--BUT OUR BEST INTEL SAYS HE DID NOT SURVIVE THE ATTACK."

OBVIOUSLY, HYDRA TAKING OVER A COUNTRY IN EASTERN EUROPE IS A CATASTROPHICALLY DESTABILIZING EVENT FOR THE REGION AND THE WORLD--

--BUT THEN WE RECEIVED THIS MESSAGE ON A SECURE CHANNEL--

GREETINGS, MEN AND WOMEN OF S.H.I.E.L.D....

1945.

IT'S BEEN SO DIFFICULT TO FIND GOOD BOTTLES DURING THIS CURSED WAR, YOU KNOW.

I'VE BEEN SAVING THIS ONE FOR A SPECIAL OCCASION--

THE HYDRA I REMEMBER WAS A PROUD, ANCIENT ORDER, ONE THAT VALUED **STRENGTH** ABOVE ALL ELSE. IT DEMANDED **SACRIFICE**.

...ROGERS?

WHAT HAVE **YOU** EVER SACRIFICED, SCHMIDT? WHEN HAVE YOU DONE ANYTHING FOR THE GLORY OF ANYTHING OTHER THAN **YOURSELF?**

GET--GET BACK, IDIOT-- I **COMMAND** IT!

I THINK I'VE LISTENED TO YOUR COMMANDS LONG ENOUGH, ACTUALLY.

SIN! CROSSBONES!

NO ONE IS GOING TO HELP YOU, SKULL-- IT'S JUST **US** NOW.

YOU DON'T REMEMBER IT, BUT A LONG TIME AGO YOU COST ME SOMETHING VERY DEAR TO MY HEART. THE THING I HAD DEDICATED MY LIFE TO. MY **PURPOSE**.

YOU TOOK IT, AND YOU TWISTED IT AND POISONED IT TO SUIT YOUR OWN SICK AIMS.

WHAT YOU DID BACK THEN PUT ME ON A DIFFERENT PATH. BUT MAYBE I SHOULD THANK YOU FOR THAT.

YOU SEE, ALL THAT SUFFERING AND SACRIFICE, IT MADE ME **STRONGER**. YOU MAY NOT UNDERSTAND THAT--

--SO LET ME SHOW YOU HOW MUCH STRONGER.

N-NO. NO--!

THIS IS EXACTLY WHAT WE WARNED ABOUT, COMMANDER CARTER--

GETTING DRAGGED INTO SOME SOKOVIAN CIVIL WAR, FIGHTING AN INSURGENCY--

I UNDERSTAND YOUR CONCERNS, COUNCILMEMBERS--

--BUT WHAT'S DONE IS DONE. NOW WE'RE LOOKING AT OUR WORST-CASE SCENARIO--HYDRA IN CONTROL OF A EUROPEAN STATE, ONE WITH **NUCLEAR CAPABILITY**. THE THREAT HAS BEEN MADE--

HAS IT? I WATCHED THE MESSAGE, I FOUND THE LANGUAGE UNCLEAR.

AS DID I. AND BESIDES, WE TOLERATED NOVOTY FOR **YEARS**. PERHAPS WE CAN SIMPLY CARRY ON--

NO--

--DO YOU **HEAR** YOURSELVES? THIS IS **HYDRA**--THE **RED SKULL'S** HYDRA. ANY BELIEF THAT WE CAN TOLERATE HIM HAVING A FOOTHOLD IN EUROPE IS A DELUSION. IF YOU SEEK TO **APPEASE** HIM, HE WILL ONLY GROW STRONGER.

I DON'T DISAGREE, COMMANDER. BUT PERHAPS IF **DIRECTOR ROGERS** WERE HERE--

I TOLD YOU--THE DIRECTOR IS ON A SECRET MISSION RIGHT NOW. EVEN **I'M** NOT PRIVY TO HIS WHERE-ABOUTS--

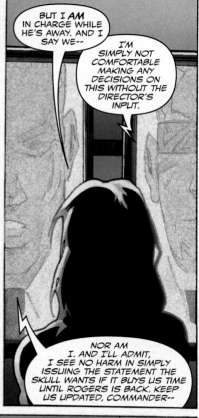

BUT I **AM** IN CHARGE WHILE HE'S AWAY. AND I SAY WE--

I'M SIMPLY NOT COMFORTABLE MAKING ANY DECISIONS ON THIS WITHOUT THE DIRECTOR'S INPUT.

NOR AM I. AND I'LL ADMIT, I SEE NO HARM IN SIMPLY ISSUING THE STATEMENT THE SKULL WANTS IF IT BUYS US TIME UNTIL ROGERS IS BACK. KEEP US UPDATED, COMMANDER--

--BUT FOR NOW, WE WAIT.

HAIL HYDRA.

WAS IT QUICK?

IT WAS.

PITY.

I STILL DON'T GET IT, THOUGH, ROGERS-- THE SKULL WAS RIGHT-- HIS PLAN DON'T WORK WITHOUT XAVIER'S BRAIN--

IT'S NOT *HIS* PLAN, CROSSBONES. IT NEVER WAS. IT'S *MINE*--

"THEY CALL IT THE COSMIC CUBE."

16

ENGLAND.
1945.

STEVEN, MY DEAR...

...YOU'VE BARELY UTTERED A WORD THE WHOLE JOURNEY. NOT THAT I MINDED ENTIRELY, I DID GET TO FINISH MY BOOK.

GERALD GARDNER, SUCH AN EXHIBITIONIST.

HOW CAN YOU *READ* AT A TIME LIKE THIS, ELISA?!

"HYDRA IS *LOST*.

"THE *RED SKULL* HAS *TAKEN* IT FROM US.

"MEANWHILE, MY BEST FRIEND IS SITTING IN AN ALLIED PRISON CELL, WAITING FOR THE *FIRING SQUAD*...

"AND ON TOP OF EVERYTHING-- NOW YOU TELL ME THE AMERICANS HAVE DEVELOPED SOME KIND OF *SUPER-WEAPON* THAT WILL HELP THEM WIN THE WAR."

YOU ASK ME WHAT I'M THINKING, ELISA...

...I'M THINKING THIS IS THE *END*.

HM. I SEE. HOW DREADFUL.

WELL, PERHAPS YOU'RE RIGHT, DARLING. BUT THEN, YOU KNOW WHAT THEY SAY: WHEN YOU THINK YOU'VE REACHED THE END--

--IT HELPS TO GO BACK TO WHERE IT ALL BEGAN.

WELCOME BACK TO *THE KEEP*, STEVEN.

WELCOME HOME.

FIXER--DOCTOR SELVIG--WHAT IS OUR PROGRESS?

UNCHANGED FROM THE **LAST** TIME YOU ASKED US FOR AN UPDATE, ZEMO.

YEAH, FIVE MINUTES AGO.

FORGIVE MY **IMPATIENCE,** FIXER.

PERHAPS IT'S DUE TO THE FACT THAT I WAS PROMISED THE CUBE **HOURS** AGO--

--OR PERHAPS IT IS BECAUSE I WATCHED YOUR MISCALCULATIONS SEND THE FRAGMENTS WE'D WORKED SO HARD TO RETRIEVE MILES AWAY, LOST TO US ACROSS THE ARCTIC!

UH-HUH, I GET IT--I SCREWED UP, FINE. BUT LOOK, WE'RE ON TOP OF IT--WE HAVE SEVEN OF THE EIGHT COSMIC CUBE FRAGMENTS BACK, LOCKED IN AND READY--

"--AND MOONSTONE AND ATLAS ARE OUT THERE LOOKING FOR THE LAST ONE RIGHT NOW."

WELL, YOU HAD BETTER HOPE THEY FIND IT SOON. WE **MUST** BUILD THAT CUBE--

AH, OR, ALTERNATIVE THESIS--WE COULD SIMPLY ALLOW THE FRAGMENT TO RECONSTITUTE AS **KOBIK,** AND CONVINCE THE GIRL TO DO WHAT YOU NEED...CERTAINLY A SIMPLER SOLUTION--

SELVIG, YOU SENTIMENTAL OLD FOOL...I AM NOT TAKING ANY MORE RISKS ON THIS "CHILD" YOU ALL SEEM SO PRECIOUS ABOUT.

SHE IS A DANGER TO US ALL. SHE HAS WREAKED NOTHING BUT **CHAOS** THROUGHOUT HER SHORT EXISTENCE.

I DO NOT NEED AN ADORABLE LITTLE RUG RAT PULLING ON MY HEART-STRINGS, YOU UNDERSTAND? I NEED **OBEDIENCE. COMPLIANCE.** SHE DOES NOT NEED SENTIENCE TO PROVIDE THOSE THINGS.

SHE ONLY NEEDS TO BE HER **TRUE SELF...**

...SHE ONLY NEEDS TO BE A *CUBE.*

NOW, IF YOU'LL EXCUSE ME--I HAVE OTHER TRULY DELIGHTFUL BUSINESS TO ATTEND TO.

AW, COME ON.

NOT AGAIN.

1945.

NOW, LET'S SEE IF WE CAN FIND A KETTLE AND AN *OPEN FLAME*, YES? I'M POSITIVELY DRAINED--

ELISA-- WHAT THE HELL IS THIS?!

WHY WOULD YOU BRING ME BACK HERE? WHY WOULD YOU WANT ME TO *SEE* THIS?

JUST SO I'D KNOW THAT EVERYTHING I EVER WORKED FOR-- EVERYTHING I EVER *FOUGHT* FOR--WAS LOST? YOU THINK I DON'T REALIZE THAT ALREADY?

HYDRA IS *RUINED*. WE THOUGHT WE COULD MANIPULATE THE REICH TO SUIT OUR WHIMS, AND INSTEAD THEY *DEVOURED US WHOLE*.

BUT THEN AGAIN, MAYBE IT'S WHAT WE *DESERVE*. MAYBE ALL OF THIS ISN'T WHAT I TOLD MYSELF IT WAS.

MAYBE IT WAS ALL A *LIE*. YOU SAID THIS WAS WHERE IT ALL BEGAN--

--BUT IT WASN'T. NOT FOR *ME*. I WASN'T BORN HERE LIKE SOME OF THE OTHERS. I WAS *BROUGHT* HERE.

AFTER YOU *TOOK* ME--

"--AFTER YOU *KILLED MY MOTHER*."

OH, STEVEN--

NO. DON'T.

IT TOOK ME *YEARS* TO ACCEPT IT. AND EVEN THEN, I TRIED TO TELL MYSELF THAT--THAT ALL OF THIS HAD HAPPENED FOR A PURPOSE. THAT SHE DIED FOR A REASON.

BUT THAT ISN'T *TRUE*, IS IT?

IT WAS JUST MADMEN THIRSTING FOR POWER. THE IDEALS, THE BELIEFS--NONE OF IT WAS *REAL*. JUST WHAT YOU TOLD THE CANNON FODDER.

AND NOW ALL THAT'S LEFT IS TO POUR SALT IN THE WOUND BEFORE YOU SEND ME OUT ON ANOTHER MISSION. PROBABLY MY *LAST*.

LET'S JUST GET ON WITH IT THEN.

-:SIGH:- MY BOY. MY LITTLE WARRIOR. DO YOU REALLY THINK *THAT'S* WHY WE CAME HERE? SO THAT I COULD *TAUNT* YOU? TORTURE YOU?

I'VE TOLD YOU SO MANY TIMES, AND YET STILL YOU REFUSE TO BELIEVE-- EVER SINCE THE DAY I FIRST LAID EYES ON YOU, I HAVE LOVED YOU LIKE YOU WERE MY OWN.

BUT YOU ARE *NOT* MY OWN. I HAVE ALWAYS UNDERSTOOD THAT.

I DIDN'T BRING YOU HERE TO GIVE YOU ANOTHER MISSION--

STEVEN?

--I BROUGHT YOU HERE SO THAT I COULD FULFILL MY PROMISE.

...MOM?

MOM-- IS IT--IS IT REALLY--?

IT'S ME.

MOM!

I CAN'T BELIEVE IT'S YOU--

I KNOW, SON--I KNOW--

ATLAS TO FIXER-- GOOD NEWS--

WE FOUND THE LAST FRAGMENT. YOU'RE WELCOME.

BRINGING IT BACK TO BASE NOW.

OH, THANK GOD. ONE MORE HOUR AND I'M PRETTY SURE ZEMO WOULD'VE LOST IT. WELL, EVEN MORE THAN USUAL.

LET'S GET IT READY--FETCH ME THE LAST CONTAINMENT UNIT.

SHE'S DOOMED, THEN...MY LITTLE GIRL...

"MY KOBIK."

I CAN'T LET THEM DO THIS TO YOU...

HEY, DOC, I DON'T LIKE IT ANY MORE THAN YOU DO, BUT WE HAVE TO GET THIS SHOW ON THE ROAD.

UH, Y-YES, SORRY--JUST LOOKING--AH, THERE WE ARE--

--I'VE FOUND IT.

I MAY NOT BE ABLE TO SAVE YOU, BUT I CAN AT LEAST GIVE YOU A CHANCE, KOBIK.

JUST HAVE TO GET YOU FAR, FAR FROM HERE...

1945.

I'M SURPRISED TO SEE YOU UP SO EARLY--

--GIVEN HOW LATE INTO THE NIGHT I HEARD ALL THE REMINISCING AND LAUGHTER.

I HOPE WE DIDN'T KEEP YOU UP...

NONSENSE, IT WAS MUSIC TO MY EARS.

SO ALL THOSE YEARS AGO--

ONE OF THOSE BRUTES THAT ACCOMPANIED ME DID IN FACT **STRIKE** HER--AND I'M SORRY FOR THAT, STEVEN. TRUST THAT HE WAS SEVERELY REPRIMANDED.

BUT IT WAS LITTLE MORE THAN A BUMP ON THE HEAD.

AND SINCE THEN, SHE'S BEEN VERY WELL-PROVIDED-FOR--

I KNOW.

AND WE KEPT HER CLOSELY INFORMED ON HOW YOU WERE DOING-- PHOTOGRAPHS, REPORT CARDS, SOME OF YOUR DRAWINGS, EVEN--

ELISA--

--I KNOW.

I ONLY WISH YOU COULD HAVE BEEN REUNITED SOONER. BUT WE KNEW IF YOU WERE TO BECOME EVERYTHING WE NEEDED YOU TO BE--

THIS HAD TO BE THE WAY. I UNDERSTAND. AND I'M SORRY FOR THE THINGS I SAID BEFORE--

NONSENSE, DEAR BOY. WE ALL FACE CRISES OF FAITH FROM TIME TO TIME.

WELL, IT'S OVER NOW.

...WHAT DO YOU NEED ME TO DO?

FIRST, YOU WILL GO FREE YOUR FRIEND HELMUT, AND HELP HIM GET THE VENGEANCE HE SO DESERVES. BUT YOU WILL TELL HIM NOTHING OF THIS MISSION.

FROM THERE, A PLANE WILL TAKE YOU FAR FROM HERE--

"--AND DEEP INTO THE PACIFIC THEATER.

"THE KRAKEN WILL GUIDE YOU FROM THERE."

THE PLACE HE WILL TAKE YOU IS THE ONE HE WAS SWORN TO PROTECT. THE SOURCE OF ALL OUR POWER. WHERE HYDRA WAS BIRTHED.

THERE, YOU WILL BE SORELY TESTED, BODY AND SOUL. BUT IT IS THE KEY TO YOUR SURVIVING THE CHANGE.

I UNDERSTAND. BUT, ELISA... IF EVERYTHING IS CHANGED--WHAT ABOUT MY *MOTHER?* HELMUT? WHAT ABOUT *YOU?*

ON THIS, THE SIGHT IS UNCLEAR. BUT KNOW THIS, STEVEN--

--I WILL CALL UPON THE ELDER GODS. I WILL CONSULT THE FORBIDDEN BOOKS. I WILL SELL MY OWN *SOUL* IF I HAVE TO. NO MATTER WHAT IT TAKES--

"--WE WILL BE TOGETHER AGAIN SOMEDAY."

NOW.

I STILL CAN'T BELIEVE IT--YOU'RE *HERE.*

I *PROMISED* YOU, DIDN'T I? YOU KNOW HOW I AM ABOUT SUCH THINGS, SILLY BOY. OH, AND I BROUGHT YOU A PRESENT.

MAY I INTRODUCE TO YOU--

--THE NEW *HIGH COUNCIL OF HYDRA.*

HAIL HYDRA.

THEY WILL STAND BY YOUR SIDE AS YOU RULE, ONCE YOUR PLAN IS REALIZED--

RIGHT-- ABOUT THE PLAN-- I'M AFRAID THERE HAVE BEEN SOME LAST-MINUTE *HICCUPS*--

YOU MEAN YOU LACK XAVIER'S BRAIN. NOT TO WORRY, MY DEAR. PRESUMING THE DIRECTOR OF S.H.I.E.L.D. CAN REACH OUT TO HIS WAITING SHIP--

UH, HEY, CAP, THAT'S WEIRD, I WAS JUST HAVING A CONVERSATION ABOUT YOU--

WITH MARIA HILL, RIGHT? WHATEVER SHE SAID--IT'S A *TRAP*, RICK. DID YOU MANAGE TO GET THE ACCESS CODES FOR THE PLANETARY DEFENSE SHIELD?

UM-- YEAH. JUST FINISHED, ACTUALLY--

AND THAT'S WHY SHE'S CALLING. SHE SET CAROL UP--GOT HER TO BUILD THE SHIELD FOR HER, WHILE SHE KEPT HER OWN OVERRIDE CODES.

WITH THE CHITAURI WAVE COMING, SHE'S PLANNING TO USE THEM AS *LEVERAGE*--FORCE THE WORLD SECURITY COUNCIL TO GIVE HER BACK HER OLD JOB--SHE'S OUT OF CONTROL--

OKAY, *THAT* ACTUALLY MAKES SENSE-- SO WE SHOULD TELL CAPTAIN MARVEL, RIGHT?

THERE'S NO TIME--THE WAVE IS INCOMING NOW! I NEED THOSE *ACCESS CODES*--

RIGHT, BUT-- BEFORE THAT, YOU SHOULD KNOW--HILL IS SAYING YOU'RE--AND BELIEVE ME, I KNOW HOW *CRAZY* THIS SOUNDS-- SHE SAID YOU WERE *HYDRA*.

RICK.

YEAH, NO, I GET IT--

"THIS IS *MARIA HILL* WE'RE TALKING ABOUT, RICK. THE SAME PERSON WHO CHASED YOU AROUND THE WORLD TRYING TO ARREST YOU WHEN YOU EXPOSED KOBIK.

"THE SAME PERSON WHO CREATED *PLEASANT HILL*. WHO HELPED START THE CIVIL WAR OVER THE REGISTRATION ACT. MADRIPOOR. LATVERIA-- DO I NEED TO KEEP GOING ON?"

YOU CAN'T TRUST HER, RICK-- *EVER*. BUT IF YOU FEEL LIKE YOU NEED TO WAIT--DESPITE THE RISKS--

NO--NO, YOU'RE RIGHT, CAP--I DON'T TRUST HER--

--I TRUST *YOU*. SENDING CODES NOW.

AW, MAN, BAD CALL. BUT HEY, IF IT MAKES YA FEEL BETTER--

--I'DA MADE THE SAME BET.

JONES IS DOWN. ALL THE CODES GO THROUGH?

YES, THIS IS EVERYTHING WE'LL NEED TO GET INSIDE...IT'S GOOD WORK. GET RICK INTO HOLDING--DO **NOT** HURT HIM.

UNDERSTOOD, WEIRD CAPTAIN HYDRA GUY. BLACK ANT OUT.

IF THAT'S ALL FINISHED, YOUR TROOPS ARE ASSEMBLED IN THE MOUNTAINS. THEY ARE WAITING TO HEAR FROM THEIR NEW LEADER.

YEAH--WE SET UP THE SCREENS, BUT THEY WON'T BE ABLE TO SEE YOUR FACE, DON'T WORRY.

GOOD.

THIS IS IT, THEN, YES? IT'S ALL FINALLY HAPPENING. YOUR PLAN IS ABOUT TO BE REALIZED--

ACTUALLY, STEVEN--

--THERE IS SOMETHING I NEED TO TELL YOU FIRST.

I CAN'T **BELIEVE** THIS! WE WERE **THIS** **CLOSE**, ELISA! AND AFTER ALL THIS-- WE FAILED. IT'S **OVER**.

CALM DOWN, STEVEN--

CALM DOWN?! HOW CAN YOU SAY CALM DOWN?! WE **LOST** THE **COSMIC CUBE FRAGMENTS!**

I **UNDERSTAND** THAT--

THEY WERE THE KEY TO EVERYTHING--TO SAVING THE WORLD THAT WAS--

I UNDERSTAND THAT, AS WELL. BUT LISTEN TO ME, STEVEN--

--WHAT'S DONE IS DONE. AND I HAVE SUFFERED TOO MUCH TO LET THIS BREAK ME NOW.

THE PLAN WAS ALWAYS TWOFOLD--CONQUER THIS WORLD AND THEN RESTORE THE OLD ONE. TO SHOW IT THE ERROR OF ITS WAYS.

NONE OF THAT NEEDS TO CHANGE.

YOU WILL **STILL** TAKE POWER. AND YOU WILL USE THAT POWER TO **FIND** THOSE FRAGMENTS AND RESHAPE THE EARTH TO YOUR WILL.

ONE MORE CHALLENGE. ONE MORE TEST. THAT'S ALL THIS IS. REMEMBER--

--THIS IS WHAT YOU WERE MEANT TO DO.

NOW, GET IN THERE. I HAVE WAITED **LIFETIMES** TO SEE YOU LEAD THIS ARMY TO VICTORY.

GO ADDRESS YOUR SOLDIERS, SUPREME LEADER--

"--YOUR REIGN IS AT HAND."

I UNDERSTAND THAT MANY OF YOU MUST BE CONFUSED RIGHT NOW--WONDERING WHO THIS MAN IS WHO CLAIMS TO BE YOUR NEW LEADER.

AND I WISH THAT I COULD SHOW YOU MY FACE, THAT I COULD LOOK YOU IN THE EYE--

--BUT THE TIME IS NOT YET RIGHT, I'M AFRAID.

THE SKULL TOLD YOU HYDRA WAS AN OUTLET FOR YOUR ANGER. HE CHANNELED YOUR RAGE TO SUIT HIS OWN ENDS--

--BUT I AM HERE TO TELL YOU THAT HYDRA IS SO MUCH MORE.

IT HAS EXISTED SINCE THE DAWN OF MAN, PERSEVERED THROUGH DYNASTIES AND EMPIRES. TO BELONG TO IT IS TO BELONG TO SOMETHING FAR GREATER THAN YOURSELVES.

COUNTLESS YEARS AGO, A WHEEL WAS BUILT, AND SEATED AROUND IT WERE THE HEADS OF BROTHERHOODS AND ORGANIZATIONS--THE SHIELD, THE SPEAR, THE LEVIATHAN--

--AND THEY WERE PITTED AGAINST ONE ANOTHER, USED AS PAWNS BY MEN WHO BELIEVED THEMSELVES TO BE ENLIGHTENED AND ELITE.

WELL, I AM HERE TO END ALL THAT. I WILL NOT BE RULED BY THE WHEEL--I WILL RULE IT INSTEAD.

AND ALL OF US WILL BE PAWNS NO LONGER.

WELCOME TO THE PLANETARY DEFENSE SHIELD BASE STATION--

PLEASE HOLD FOR IDENTISCAN

"I WILL NOT LIE TO YOU LIKE THE SKULL DID--

"--THE PATH IN FRONT OF US IS NOT ANY EASY ONE.

JAMES Q. REED
S.H.I.E.L.D. TECHNICAL SUPPORT
CLEAR FOR ENTRY

"IT WILL BE DIFFICULT, AND TREACHEROUS--

HAIL HYDRA!

"--AND ALL OF US WILL BE CALLED UPON TO SACRIFICE.

"BUT KNOW THAT WE ARE STRIVING FOR SOMETHING WORTHY...

"UNITED, WE WILL ACHIEVE THE IMPOSSIBLE.

CAPTAIN MARVEL-- SHIELD'S DOWN, MA'AM!

WHAT?! THE WAVE HASN'T EVEN HIT YET--

INCOMING

NOT THE WAVE, MA'AM-- SOMEONE'S HIT THE BASE STATION!

"KNOW THAT I WILL NEVER ASK FROM YOU WHAT I AM NOT WILLING TO DO MYSELF.

"I HAVE GIVEN EVERYTHING TO THIS CAUSE--

STEVE...

"--AND I HAVE PAID A TERRIBLE PRICE.

"BUT I WILL NEVER WAVER, AND I EXPECT THE SAME FROM YOU--OUR VICTORY IS AT HAND!"

"WE WILL EXPOSE THOSE WHO CLAIM TO LEAD US--WE WILL LAY BARE THEIR WEAKNESS, AND THEIR CORRUPTION!"

"WE WILL BRING ORDER AND STRENGTH TO THE CHAOS!"

"THIS IS THE HOUR, THIS IS THE PLACE--NOW, EVERYTHING CHANGES--"

"--AND WHEN IT'S OVER, WHEN THE DUST SETTLES--THE WHOLE WORLD WILL KNEEL AND SAY THE WORDS..."

Captain America: Steve Rogers 16 & Captain America: Sam Wilson 21 connecting variants by
R.B. SILVA & MARTE GRACIA